Sunset Puppy Party

Janis Miller Lightman
Mark Shannon

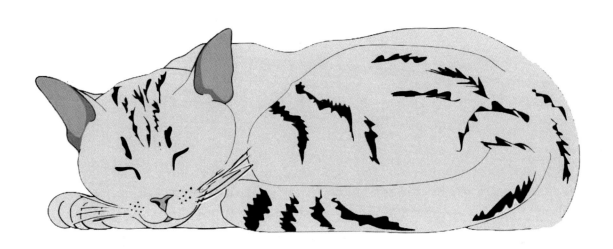

This is a book about puppies, the title tells you that -

But don't be suprised if you see a hidden cat!

SUNSET PUPPY PARTY

Self published in the U.S.
by
Janis Miller Lightman

This book is a work of non-fiction taken from real life events as experienced and remembered by the author. Some names and identifying characteristics may have been changed to enhance the reading experience. The illustrations are based on the author's interpretation of events and characters as she recalls them, and are not to be taken as true or accurate representations of the people and animals in the story. The illustrations of people leaving the park are a combination of free use clipart provided with the illustration software and original drawings. Any resemblance to persons living or dead is unintentional and purely coincidental.

Dedicated with love to Jonathan and Susie -

Each day before dark, boys and girls leave the park.

And after they do,
Puppy Party starts
anew.

Olive arrives, she's as sweet as honey. She enjoys a nice rub on her soft and bright tummy.

Then comes Benny, who leads his friend Bob. True love between man and his best friend dog.

Here is Sully, all smiley
and calm.
He greets each puppy
with his paw
and his mom.

Along comes Savannah,
a new sweater to show—

The Belle of the Ball
with her big brother Beau.

Now Callie
shows up and
she's no
fearful pup.

She'll chase the wild turkeys until they fly up!

Here is Sam, he loves
to play ball. He'll run,
and he'll fetch,

and beg
treats from
us all.

...Will follow the pizza man to far Timbuktu.

They say
that Flash is part
kangaroo. He'll
jump over Benny,
Clay, Savannah and you!

Cookie dribbles and kicks on the pitch the whole day. Soccer's her sport and her best kind of play.

Meatball warms up with stair bowling today. He climbs and he tumbles down the stairs and hallway.

Cocoa and Cooper are here in the park. They'll gobble loose scraps until it gets dark

He runs and he jumps
so high in the air!

So far off the ground, then
he lands with such flair!

And it's time to eat dinner from
a bowl on a tray.

The doggies walk home
wagging tails all the way.

The puppies are home, I'm so happy to say.

Now it's time for the cool cats to come out and play

"This book made me sneak out of my yard and sniff my way to the fun"
  - Flash, the mini BernieDoodle (Bernese Mountain dog, mini poodle)

"Puppy Party is my favorite catwalk. Best booking my modeling agency has ever gotten me."
  - Savannah, the mini LabraDoodle (Labrador Retriever, poodle)

"Thanks for showcasing my athletic talent, but I really should be in the Olympics."
  - Cookie, the Toy Border Collie

"Nice to see my hunting talents featured"
  - Callie (Dachsund, Shih-Tzu and Terrier mix)

"We're finally being appreciated for all that ball throwing and frisbee work we demand."
  -Bodie, Benny and Sam, the Border Collie Trio

"Who wouldn't follow a pizza truck?"
  - Gizmo, the Chug (Chihuaha Pug)

"Best book I ever ate"
  - Cooper, the mini CavaPoo (Cavalier King Charles Spaniel, poodle)

Made in United States
Orlando, FL
02 May 2022